La Roche/Hürzeler · Schpiik you Englisch?

«Blödelei à l'anglaise».
Gesammelt von Nora La Roche
und karikaturistisch nachempfunden
von Peter Hürzeler.

Edition Erpf · Bern und München

1. Auflage   1.– 3. Tausend   Oktober 1982
2. Auflage   4.– 6. Tausend   November 1982
3. Auflage   7.– 9. Tausend   Dezember 1982
4. Auflage 10.–14. Tausend   Februar 1983
5. Auflage 15.–20. Tausend   März 1984

«Schpiik you Englisch?»

So deutsch, englischer geht's nicht...

Schpiik you Englisch? Yes, good? Dann sträuben
sich Ihnen sicher die Haare zu Berge. Denn
top-englisch klingt diese Frage ja nicht. Auch die
von Peter Hürzeler cartoonistisch nachempfundenen
Sprüche in diesem Büchlein sind nicht ganz
(schul-)stubenrein. Oder doch? Nehmen Sie unseren
John Bull doch einmal buchstäblich beim Wort. Er
speakt nämlich englischer als englisch – und somit
richtig falsch.

Die «Blödelei à l'anglaise» hat, so hält sich hartnäckig
ein Gerücht, ein ehemaliger deutscher Bundes-
präsident salonfähig gemacht. Bei einem Staats-
empfang soll er der englischen Königin zugeflüstert
haben: «Equal goes it loose.» Und so ging's gleich
los: an Parties, in Büros, bei Business-Lunches.
Aus der Blödelei wurde ein Gesellschaftsspiel.

Nora La Roche und Peter Hürzeler haben für Sie die
ausgefallensten (Un-)Sinnsprüche in diesem Büchlein
zusammengefasst.

Equal goes it loose...

Zürich, Sommer 1982   *Edith Lier*

WHO OTHERS
A PIT DIGS,
FALLS HIMSELF
INTO !

IT IS NOT
TO CATCH
WHAT FOR A LONG
LEADING
YOU HAVE

IN THE
SHORTNESS
LIES THE
SPICE .

CUT OFF !
THE BULLS
DIVE UP !

THE MOST
SUNDAY CHILDREN
ARE LUCKY
MUSHROOMS

WHO
OTHERS IN THE
NOSE DIGS
IS SELF
A PIG

You MEAN
I HAVE NOT ALL
CUPS
IN THE CLOSET?
FAR MISSED,
FAR MISSED!

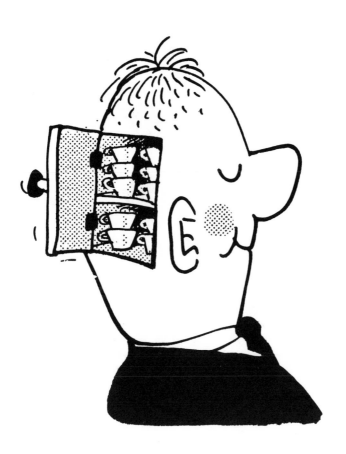

BE NOT SO
UNASHAMED !
OR I SHOW YOU
WHERE
THE HAMMER
HANGS !

HOLY STRAWBAG!
MAKE
NOT ALWAYS A
TWENTY-AFTER-
EIGHT-SNOUT!

CARE
FOR NUMBERRICH
AFTERGROWTH .
IT MAKES
THE CHILDRENCAR-
INDUSTRY
HAPPY .

THE TALES
OF YOUR SIDE-JUMPS
GO ME
MIGHTY ON THE
ALARM-CLOCK!

YESTERDAY
SHE GAVE ME AN
EARFIG.
NOW I HAVE THE
NOSE FULL OF
HER.

NOTHING
OTHER STAYS
ME LEFT :
I AM
AND STAY A
SLIPPER- HERO

THIS
CURLS NO DOG
BEHIND
THE OVEN
BEFORE !

YOUR
UPMAKING AT
JIM'S PARTY
FELL COMPLETELEY
OUT
OF THE FRAME

I GET
FOX-DEVIL'S WILD
IF YOU MAKE
ME TO THE
PIG !

WHAT HE SAID
WAS A LIQUOR-IDEA
AND WENT FULLY
INTO
THE TROUSERS

MAKE NOT
SO A THICK NECK-
OR I GIVE YOU
A COUPLE
BEHIND THE
SPOONS

WITH YOU
IS NOT GOOD
CHERRY
EATING

THE EVENINGLY
HOMEWAY
IN THE PUSHTIME
MAKES ME
NOODLE FINISHED

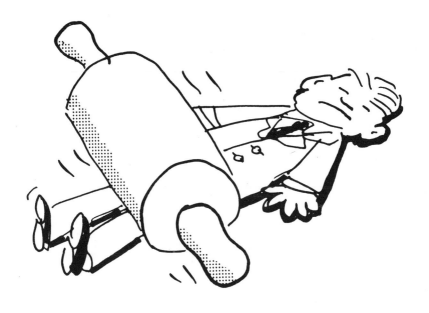

HE IS
A HARE – FOOT
AND
BEYOND OF GOOD
AND NASTY

I HAVE YET A LITTLE CHICKEN WITH YOU TO PLUCK

HE IS QUITE
OUT
OF THE LITTLE
HOUSE

HE MAKES
HER HOTLY THE
COURT
AND SHE SHOWS
HIM THE
COLD SHOULDER

STOP

HACKING AROUND

ON ME

PLAY NOT
THE
OFFENDED
LIVERSAUSAGE

WHO COMES
ON THE DOG
KNOWS,
THAT ALL WAS
FOR THE CAT.

WHAT TOO FAR
GOES,
GOES TOO FAR!
AND THIS GOES
OVER THE
HAT-STRING!

SLOWLY
BUT SHURELY
THIS ALL
HANGS US TO
THE NECK
OUT